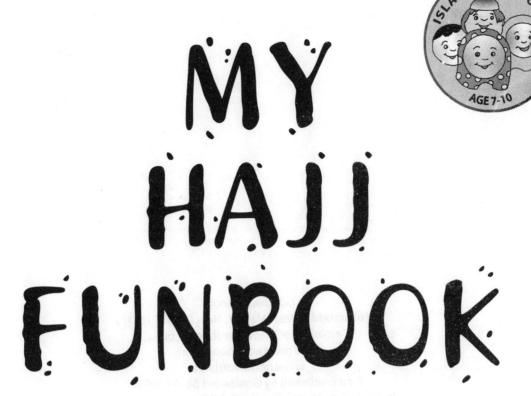

MY HAJJ FUNBOOK

ISLAMIC FUNBOOKS
AGE 7-10

**PUZZLES
CROSSWORDS
WORDSEARCHES
COLORING
AND MANY OTHER ACTIVITIES**

by
TAHERA KASSAMALI

Goodword**kidz**

Helping you build a family of faith

D1275346

Goodword Books
1, Nizamuddin West Market, New Delhi-110 013
email: info@goodwordbooks.com
www.goodwordbooks.com
www.goodword.net
First published by Goodword Books 2003
in arrangement with Tayyiba Publishers & Distributors
Reprinted 2010
© Goodword Books 2010
Printed in India

MY HAJJ FUNBOOK

Children need to be taught Islam in a way which takes into consideration the mind of a child. Learning about religion is sometimes taken as serious and even boring. In order to change that negative conception, educators and parents need to use more appealing methods to put the message of Islam across to the younger generation. Islamic Funbooks are designed with that purpose in mind, and we hope that both parents and children will enjoy going through it.

For the Parent

Our experience shows that no book or teacher can take the place of a parent when it comes to teaching children religious beliefs and practices. We urge that parents use this book as a tool in their efforts to help their children understand and appreciate Islam. Please note the following points:

1. The activities in this book cater for different levels. Some children may be able to do them easily, while some may require help with a few pages. Work together with your child through these pages to encourage an enthusiasm for learning and thinking about Islamic teachings.

2. The answers to many of the activities are given at the end of the book. Let the child complete the activities and THEN refer to the answers. It would be beneficial if the child read and re-read the book to get the answers, rather than look directly at the answer pages.

3. Some of the exercises require a reference to the Qur'an. Obtain a Qur'an with a simple translation for your child. Referring to the Qur'an will, Inshallah, encourage an interest in its contents, and an appreciation for the holy Book.

4. The transliteration for many Arabic words such as Zilhajj, Zabiha, Sa'ee etc. are according to what is found normally. These may not be strictly correct but are easier for children to understand.

Please continue to encourage your child to learn more about Islam. To instill an appreciation for religious beliefs and practices in a young mind is the most rewarding thing you can do for your child. The effects could last a lifetime.

Zilqa`d 1416/March 1996
Tayyiba Publishers
P.O.Box 88003 Lansdowne Mall Richmond B.C. Canada V6X 3T6

A Hajj Dictionary

Arafat. A long and wide open place where pilgrims go on the 9th of Zilhijjah. They stay thee till sunset, worshipping Allah. The mountain of mercy is in Arafat.

Hajar The black stone in the Ka'bah which was brought from Heaven.

Ihram. Special clothes of the pilgrims. The Ihram is two pieces of white unsewn material for men and white simple clothes for women.

Maqam Ibrahim. A Stone near the Ka'bah with the footprint of Nabi Ibrahim on it. Pilgrims recite the prayer after Tawaf beside it.

Mina. The pilgrims go tc Mina on the 10th Zilhijjah. Here they will throw 7 pebbles at each of the three pillars, carry out the sacrifice and cut off part of their hair or nails as Taqseer.

Miqat. A place from where the pilgrims put on the Ihram.

Muzdalifah. The pilgrims go to Muzdalifah at sunset on the 9th of Zilhijjah. They stay for the night there, and collect pebbles for use in Mina.

Sacrifice. On the 10th of Zilhijjah, pilgrims sacrifice an animal in the memory of the sacrifice of Nabi Ibrahim (a).

Sa'ee. Every pilgrim has to run seven times between Safa and Marwah, the two hills near the Ka'bah.

Talbiyah. The pilgrims recite the Talbiyah as part of the Ihram.

Taqseer. After finishing the rituals of hajj, pilgrims cut off part of their hair or nails.

Wuqoof. The staying in Arafat is known as Wuqoof.

Guidance from the Qur'an

The Holy Qur'an is a book of guidance. It has come from Allah to help us have a better life, in the world and in the hereafter. Do you know what Allah says about Hajj in the Qur'an? Read the following verses to find out.

And (remember) when We made the House, a place of assembly for mankind, and a place of safety, and take the standing place of Ibrahim as a place for prayer. And We gave a duty to Ibrahim and Isma`il saying: Purify My House for those who visit it, and those who cling to it, and those who bow down, and those who prostrate.

(2:125)

Most surely the first house appointed for mankind is the one at Bekka, blessed and a guidance for the nations. In it are clear signs; the standing place of Ibraheem, and whoever enters it shall be secure. Pilgrimage to the house is a duty on mankind for the sake of Allah, on everyone who is able to undertake the journey. And whoever disbelieves, Allah is self-Sufficent, above the needs of the world.

(3:96-7)

And announce among mankind the pilgrimage; they will come to you on foot, and on every lean camel, coming from every remote path. That they may witness advantages for them and mention the name of Allah during the stated days, over the cattle which He has provided them, then eat of them, and feed the distressed one, the needy.   (22:27-8)

5

Answer the following Questions.

(Refer to the other pages in this book for help)

Circle the most correct answer.

1. Bekka is another name for:
a) The Ka'bah.
b) Mecca.
c) Masjidul Haram.

2. The standing place of Ibrahim is:
a) Musalla Ibrahim.
b) Hijr Isma`il.
c) Maqam Ibrahim.

3. Pilgrims say the prayer at the standing place of Ibrahim after doing the:
a) Tawaf.
b) Sa'ee
c) Taqseer.

4. Allah refers to the Ka'bah as "My House". So the Ka'bah is also called:
a) Bait al-Qadeem
b) Baitullah.
c) Masjidul Haram

Fill in the blanks.

1. Allah says pilgrimage is a duty on one who is able to go. Can you think of two things which a Muslim should have so he can go for Hajj?
_____ and _____

2. The name of Allah is mentioned during the pilgrimage on some appointed days. What days are these?
From the _____ to the _____ of _____ (month).

3. Who should be fed from the animal which is sacrificed during Hajj? The _____ and the _____ .

Write whether the following sentences are True or False.

1. Allah told Nabi Ibrahim and Nabi Isma`il to purify His house for the people who lived around the Ka'bah. _____

2. A pilgrim who sacrifices an animal in Hajj cannot eat from it. _____

3. The Ka'bah is a blessed place and whoever goes there will be safe. _____

The Ka'bah

Answer the following questions to test your knowledge on the Ka'bah. You may choose your answers from the box below.

1. What does the word Ka'bah mean? _____

2. Who built the Ka'bah?

_____ and _____

3. The Ka'bah is covered with a black cloth with verses of the Holy Qur'an emroidered on it in golden thread. What is this cloth known as?

_____

4. What is the name of the special stone set in the Ka'bah?

_____

5. Where did this stone come from?

_____

6. What is the Mosque surrounding the Ka'bah known as?

_____

Hajar al-Aswad	Kiswah	Masjidul Haram
Nabi Isma'il	Cube	Nabi Ibrahim	Heaven

The Qibla

The Ka'bah is the Qibla for all Muslims around the world. That means that every Muslim, in whatever part of the world, turns towards the Ka'bah when he prays. The Ka'bah is thus the centre of the Muslim world.

Can you answer the questions in the following boxes?

What was the Qibla of the Muslims when they first began to pray?

_____

What can you use to find out the direction of the Qibla from wherever you are?

_____

Name two other times when Muslims must face the Qibla

1. _____

_____

2. _____

_____

What happens if you turn away from the Qibla when you are praying?

_____

_____

What would happen if there was no Qibla for prayers and Muslims could pray in any direction they wished?

Missing Letters

The following is the story of Ahmed when he saw the Ka'bah for the first time. He was very excited about it, and wrote a story to share his experience with his friends. Some vowels, however, are missing. Look at the vowels at the top of the page, and then fill them in the right places.

My visit to the Ka'bah
By Ahmed Dawood

Last year my parents decided to go for Umra. I begg _ d them to take me as I was very eager to see the h _ ly places I had always heard about. They agre _ d, and we left for Jeddah on December 5th, 1995. Upon reaching Jedd _ h, we set off for Mecca. We stopped at one of the M _ qats to put on our Ihr _ m. It was only two piec _ s of unsewn mater _ al, and I w _ s afraid that it would f _ ll off. I did not worry too long as I was v _ ry excited. I could hardly wa _ t to see the Ka'b _ h. It was v _ ry hot and I wondered h _ w so many people were will _ ng to bear this terrible h _ at to vis _ t the house of Allah. But wh _ n I saw the Ka'bah I realized why. It was a magnific _ nt sight! All my life I had just se _ n pictur _ s of it, in b _ oks, wall hang _ ngs, etc. Now I was actually bef _ re it, and it was an awesome s _ ght. It looked so beaut _ ful, with its bright bl _ ck cloth and gold _ n writing ar _ und it. I thought of Proph _ t Ibraheem who bu _ lt it, and all the other Pr _ phets who h _ d visit_ d it. It felt so sp _ cial to be th _ re, and I felt te _ rs in my ey _ s. This was the h _ liest house of Islam, and I was extremely lucky to be able to v _ sit it. I hope and pr _ y that all of you w _ ll visit it one d _ y.

A Stone from Heaven

The Holy Ka'bah has a stone from Heaven in it. Unscramble the letters in the boxes below to find the name of that stone.

A R H J A

_____

L A

_____

D A A W S

_____

NOW FILL IN THE BLANKS BELOW

The name of the stone means "The _____".

It was brought down from heaven by _____.

Pilgrims begin and end each round of _____ at it.

It is Mustahab to _____ or _____ this stone

while going around the Ka'bah.

A Special Footprint

Near the Ka'bah, there is a stone with a special footprint on it.
Write the first letter of each of the following pictures to get the name
of that stone. Then answer the questions below.

_____ _____ _____ _____ _____

_____ _____ _____ _____ _____ _____ _____

1. Whose footprint is on that special stone?

2. What was he doing while standing on that stone?

3. What do pilgrims do beside that stone after Tawaf?

Actions of a Haji

Find out some actions carried out by a Haji in the wordsearch below. To help you find these actions, look at the flowers below

```
A  T  H  O  P  U  Y  R  O  A  T  E
B  A  K  I  P  I  H  R  A  S  U  J
O  W  L  H  V  O  E  S  D  V  F  T
S  A  L  R  P  F  D  E  H  T  O  P
K  F  T  A  L  B  I  Y  I  A  H  L
J  O  I  M  L  D  O  I  Y  Q  E  R
I  K  S  O  C  P  T  R  Y  S  B  V
P  S  A  C  R  I  F  I  U  E  N  H
O  P  E  J  H  Y  T  R  C  E  R  W
F  O  E  R  T  U  I  O  D  R  S  T
L  W  T  D  E  E  W  U  I  P  S  E
```

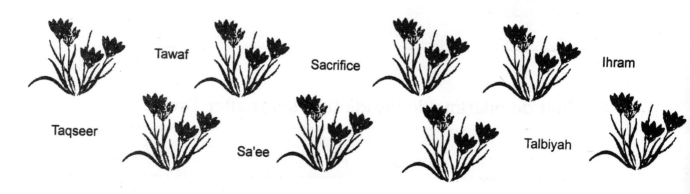

Tawaf

Sacrifice

Ihram

Taqseer

Sa'ee

Talbiyah

12

Grandma tells a story

Everyone loves a good story. Samirah and her sister Ruqayyah loved stories too. They especially loved stories told by their grandma. She made them sound so interesting. They could almost picture what she was saying, she made it sound so real. And after she finished, she asked them questions to make sure they had listened well. Join Samirah and Ruqayyah for a story telling session at Grandma's home. Then answer the questions.

Today, said Grandma, I am going to tell you a story about the Ka'bah and the Holy Prophet (s). Listen well, for you will learn many things from it.

One day, a long long time ago, when the Holy Prophet (s) was only thirty years old, the Quraysh decided to repair the Holy Ka'bah. Because of floods and storms, the Ka'bah was damaged. All the tribes were eager to have the honor of repairing the Ka'bah, and so each of them took on the task of repairing one part of the Ka'bah.

First, they took down the damaged parts, until only the pillars that Nabi Ibrahim had built were left. Then they started rebuilding it. Each tribe worked hard to make sure they built firm and strong walls for the Ka'bah. The weather was hot and dry, but the tribes worked on. When it was finished they gazed at their work proudly. They had done a good job. It was now time to put on the Hajar al-Aswad in its place. But they could not all put it together. One of them would have to do it. Each tribe wanted the honor of doing that. Confusion arose as no-one could decide who would have the special task of placing the Hajar al-Aswad.

The confusion turned into a harsh argument. The people were ready to do battle to win the special honor. Nobody wanted to allow another to do the task. The Quraysh were known to fight long battles over small arguments, and many were afraid that the fight over the Hajar al-aswad could become just that; a long unnecessary battle.

Finally one wise man came up with a solution. " I have a suggestion" he said. "Let us wait to see who will be the first to enter the Mosque today. We shall tell him to

13

decide, and whatever he says will be accepted **by all of us**". Everyone agreed as it seemed a reasonable suggestion. Now they all turned towards the entrance to see who it would be who came first to the Mosque.

Who would come along, but the Prophet Muhammad (s) himself. This event took place before the Prophet announced his Prophethood, but the people respected him for his honesty and trustworthiness. "Here comes al-Amin" shouted one of the Quraysh excitedly. "Yes! Let Muhammad decide" said another "we can trust him as we always have". They explained their problem to the Prophet. He told them not to worry as he would help them solve it.

"Get me a piece of cloth" he said. They were surprised, but did as they were told. The Prophet spread out the cloth, and placed the Hajar al-Aswad on it. Then he asked each of the leaders of the tribes to take a corner of the cloth and lift it up. When this was done, and the cloth was raised to the point where the Hajar al-Aswad was to be placed, the Prophet himself took the stone and put it in its place.

The Quraysh smiled at one another. Everyone was satisfied and a bitter fight had been avoided. Thank you, they said. You have indeed solved the problem well.

Grandma's Questions

So, said Grandma, I think you have enjoyed the story. Let me see if you were listening.

(Try to answer these questions without reading the story again)

1. How old was the Prophet when he solved the problem of re-building the Ka'bah? _____

2. What special task did each of the tribe want to do?

_____

3. What title had the Quraysh given the Prophet (s) before he announced his Prophethood? _____

4. What was the Prophet's suggestion to solve the problem of the Quraysh?

_____

_____

_____

A Train full of Pilgrims

The train below is full of young Muslims going for Hajj. These pilgrims will visit many different places. Can you find these places in the wordsearch?

```
A  W  Y  O  U  I  S  D  O  T
H  U  P  M  E  C  C  A  R  S
B  L  E  U  F  E  R  R  F  V
M  E  D  Z  K  I  O  A  G  H
Q  J  E  D  D  A  H  F  M  O
N  I  O  A  I  B  N  A  E  P
T  Y  V  L  V  M  U  H  D  S
J  D  F  I  O  Z  I  L  I  H
T  U  W  F  C  K  M  N  N  E
B  Y  I  A  M  Z  E  S  A  R
J  M  I  H  I  E  D  I  K  A
B  V  Y  U  I  O  P  T  R  S
```

15

The Talbiyah

The Talbiyah is recited by a pilgrim as part of the wajibat of Ihram. Groups of pilgrims recite it together when they travel to Mecca after the Miqat. Read the Talbiyah and its meaning below. Can you memorize it? It's not too long!

لَبَّيْكَ اَللّهُمَّ لَبَّيْكَ لَبَّيْكَ لاَ شَرِيْكَ لَكَ لَبَّيْكَ
اِنَّ الْحَمْدَ وَ النِّعْمَةَ لَكَ وَ الْمُلْكَ لاَ شَرِيْكَ لَكَ

TRANSLITERATION

Labbaik Allahumma Labbaik Labbaik La shareeka laka labbaik. Innal hamda wan ne'mata laka wal mulk, la shareeka laka.

TRANSLATION

Here I am, O Lord! here I am. Here I am, You have no partner. Here I am. Surely all praise, and blessings are for You. And the Kingdom. You have no partner.

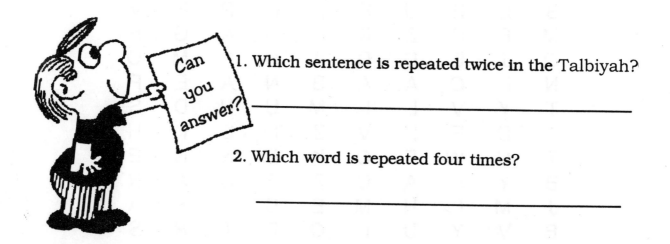

1. Which sentence is repeated twice in the Talbiyah?

_____

2. Which word is repeated four times?

_____

16

A Lesson on IHRAM

Sister Aasiya is teaching a lesson on Ihram. Read her notes and then answer the quiz on the next page. Do you think the quiz is easy or hard? Write what you think on the next page.

The word Ihram means sacred. A pilgrim is in the state of Ihram when doing the Hajj or Umrah. Ihram is also the name of the clothes of the pilgrim.

Before wearing the Ihram, a pilgrim does the ghusl. Then the niyyah is said. The niyyah has to specify the type of pligrimage.

For men Ihram is two large pieces of unsewn cloth. One is worn around the waist and reaches the knees. The other is worn over the left shoulder. The head should be uncovered.

For women Ihram is plain clothes which cover the whole body. The head is covered, but the face must be uncovered.

Once a pilgrim puts on the Ihram he is in a holy state. Certain things are forbidden for him/her These things are only allowed once the Ihram is taken off after Hajj.

Among the things haram for pilgrims in Ihram are:
a) To use perfume.
b) Kill or harm any animals or insects.
c) Wear shoes which cover the ankles.
d) Destroy plants.

Ihram must be worn at a place before reaching Mecca. These places are called Miqat. There are different Miqats for pilgrims coming from different directions.

There are three wajib things in Ihram:
a) The Niyyah
b) The Talbiyah
c) Wearing of the clothes of Ihram.

17

Sister' Aasiya's quiz on Ihram

Name:_____   Date:_____

Question I   Fill in the Blanks

1. When going for _____ or _____ a pilgrim must wear Ihram.
2. _____ must be said before wearing the Ihram.
3. Men wear _____ pieces of cloth for Ihram.
4. Women must cover their _____ and their _____ when in Ihram.
5. _____ and _____ are forbidden for pilgrims in Ihram.

Question Two   Which of the following people are wearing the Ihram correct? Put a ✓ if the Ihram is correct, and a ✗ if the Ihram is wrong.

1. Qasim wears his white sunhat in Ihram as he thinks it is too hot.
2. Samirah wears her new shoes while she does the Tawaf.
3. Sarah covers her hair with a scarf during Ihram.
4. Adil kills a mosquito who is troubling him while he is trying to sleep.
5. Bilal wears his Ihram at his hotel in Mecca and then goes for Tawaf.

Wow! That quiz was really

_____

The Tawaf

Read the following boxes of information on Tawaf. Then answer the questions.

How to do the Tawaf

1. Tawaf means to go around the Ka'bah seven times.
2. The Ka'bah should be on the left of the pilgrim when Tawaf is being done.
3. Each round of Tawaf begins and ends at the Hajar al-Aswad
4. Two rak'aat prayer must be recited after the Tawaf.

Mustahab actions of Tawaf

1. To touch or kiss the Hajar al-Aswad in Tawaf.
2. To recite verses of Qur'an or other Dhikr (rememberance) of Allah.
3. To raise the hands and salute the black stone.

Du`a recited during Tawaf

Many Du`as can be recited. One of the common ones is the following:

رَبَّنَآ اٰتِنَا فِي الدُّنْيَا حَسَنَةً وَ فِي الْأَخِرَةِ حَسَنَةً وَ قِنَا عَذَابَ النَّارِ

Our Lord! Give us good in this world and good in the Hereafter, and save us from the punishment of the fire.   (2: 201)

Different Tawafs

1. The Tawaf performed by a pilgrim when he first reaches Mecca.
2. The Tawaf done by a pilgrim after returning to Mecca from Mina.
3. Tawaf al-Widah. The Tawaf done by a pilgrim before he leaves Mecca to go home.
4. Mustahab Tawafs. Pilgrims also perform other mustahab Tawafs.

1. It is _____ to salute the black stone in Tawaf.
2. Tawaf al- _____ is the last Tawaf a pilgrim will perform before he goes home.
3. _____ should be recited while doing Tawaf.
4. Two tawafs would mean that a pilgrim goes around the Ka'bah _____ times.
5. _____ must be recited after every Tawaf.
6. What two things do pilgrims ask for in the Du`a commonly recited during Tawaf? _____

Safa and Marwah

> Surely Safa and Marwah are among the signs of Allah. So whoever makes a pilgrimage to the House of Allah, or makes a visit to it, he should go around them both. And whoever does good   then surely Allah is Appreciating, Knowing.
>
> (Sural al-Baqarah, 2:158)

Near the Ka'bah there are two hills called Safa and Marwah. When Nabi Ibrahim took his wife Hajrah and baby son Ism`ail, and left them in the valley of Mecca according to the order of Allah, there was nobody there in Mecca. No people, no animals, no food and no water! Bibi Hajrah was very worried because her baby was thirsty. When he started crying, she begun to run in search of water. She ran seven times between the two hills of Safa and Marawah. All the while she was praying to Allah that He should look after their needs. When she returned to her baby she saw that he had rubbed his feet in the sand. Under his feet sprang a well of gushing water. Thankfully Bibi Hajrah and her baby drank from that water. Later many people came and settled there because of the well.

The well which sprang up under the feet of Nabi Ism`ail is known as ZamZam. Pilgrims drink from it and sometimes take the water of ZamZam to their homes for their relatives and friends.

Every pilgrim has to walk seven times between the hills of Safa and Marwah after Tawaf. This is known as Sa`ee. While walking, the pilgrim recites verses of the Qur'an, or Du`a, and remembers Allah. The pilgrims also remember the trust in Allah that Hajrah had, and how Allah listened to her prayers. Whoever trusts in Allah will surely be successful as Allah will never let him down.

Draw the hills of Safa and Marwa and the well of ZamZam in the box below. Don't forget to label your drawing!

The Office for Informing pilgrims about Arafat requests all pilgrims to read the following page carefully before entering Arafat for Wuqoof. Please sign the paper for our records.

Welcome to Arafah

History of Arafat

The word "Arafah" means to know. It has been reported that Nabi Adam and Bibi Hawwa reunited and recognized each other in this plain, after leaving Heaven. Nabi Ibraheem has passed here, and stayed for Wuqoof. The Holy Prophet (s) also did the wuqoof in Arafat and has said that there can be no Hajj without the wuqoof in Arafat.

Please read the following instructions carefully.

1. You must be in Arafat at least by the noon of the ninth of Zilhijjah.
2. You may come to Arafat on the 8th of Zilhajj. This day is known as the day of Tarwiyah.
3. If you are ill or old or have some problem, you may come to Arafat earlier.
4. Arafat is a very wide plain. You may stay in any part of it. Please be considerate of all the other Muslims around you.

While you are in Arafat:
1. Recite as much as you can of Du'as and Dhikr of Allah.
2. Ask forgiveness for your sins.
3. Remember the day of Judgement. On that day there will also be crowds of people gathered on a field to be judged for their deeds.
4. If you can, sit near or on the Jabal ar-Rahmah, the mountain of Mercy. Pray that Allah may be merciful to you. There will be many pilgrims on the mountain, so watch your step.

After finishing the Wuqoof in Arafat, please proceed to Muzdalifa

> I have read and understood the instructions for Wuqoof in Arafat
> Date _____ Signature _____

Mina and Muzdalifah

MUZDALIFA

A place between Arafat and Mina. On the 9th of Zilhijjah, pilgrims go to Muzdalifah from Arafat, and spend the night there. They gather pebbles for throwing at the three pillars in Mina. Each pilgrim gathers 49 pebbles if he is going to stay two days in Mina (from the 10th-12th) or 70 pebbles if he is going to stay three days (upto the 13th). It is mustahab to spend the night in worship and prayer while at Muzdalifa.

MINA

Mina is a a small town 3 miles from Mecca. Nobody lives there but every year thousands of pilgrims come to stay there for two or three days.

Importance in History

1. The place where Nabi Ibrahim brought his son Isma`il to sacrifice him according to the command of Allah.
2. It used to be a meeting place for trades and fairs for the Arabs before Islam.
3. Very close to Mina is a place called Aqabah. Here the people of Medina first pledged their loyalty to the Prophet (s). Later they invited him to come toMedina which resulted in the Hijrah.

What do pilgrims do in Mina?

Pilgrims arrive in Mina on the morning of the 10th of Zilhijjah.
They will carry out the following actions:

1. Rami al Jamaraat (stoning the pillars)
In the centre of Mina there are three pillars known as Jamaraat.
The biggest of these is known as the Jamarah al-Aqaba.
Each of the Jamaraat represent the Shaytan when he came to stop Nabi Ibrahim from carrying out the sacrifice.
10th of Zilhijjah: Stoning the Jamarah al-Aqaba with 7 pebbles.
11th and 12th of Zilhijjah: Stoning each of the three jamaraat. First the pilgrims stone Jamarah al-Ula, then Jamarah al-Wusta, and finally Jamarah al-Aqabah.
13th fo Zilhijjah: If the pilgrims stay in Mina on the 13th, they stone all three pillars again.

2. Zabiha
On the 10th of Zilhijjah all pilgrims sacrifice an animal in Mina.

3. Taqseer
All pilgrims will cut some hair, or nails. Some men shave off all their hair.

Hajj  Math

1. Sameer is going to stay 3 days in Mina. He is collecting his pebbles in Muzdalifa. He wants to collect 10 extra pebbles so that if he loses some, he will still have enough for all the pillars. How many pebbles will he need?

2. If Sameer collects for himself as well as his sister, how many pebbles will he need? His sister is very careful and does not think she will need any extra pebbles. How many pebbles must Sameer collect for himself and his sister?

3. Khadijah is going to leave Mina on the 12th of Zilhijjah. How many pebbles will she need?

4. Kareem is also leaving Mina on the 12th of Zilhijjah. He is collecting pebbles in Muzdalifa with his father and mother. How many pebbles will the family collect?

5. Anisah had pebbles enough for three days in Mina. However on the way to Mina, she lost some. Now she has only 55. How many pebbles did Anisah lose?

7. During his stay in Mecca, Amin has completed 21 rounds of Tawaf. How many complete Tawafs has he done?

6. Maryam is completing her 2nd round of Tawaf. She wants to do a mustahab Tawaf after she finishes this Tawaf and recites the prayer for it. How many more rounds must she do to complete both Tawafs?

23

Shaytan - the enemy of mankind

Do you know about a great enemy of yours, who is always trying to get you into trouble with Allah? Let's read some verses of the Qur'an about him

Shaytan vows to lead the human being astray

My Lord .. I will surely make (evil) seem good to them on earth, and I will cause them all to stray, except Your devoted servants.

(15:39-40)

Shaytan lies in wait

. . I will surely lie in wait for them in Your straight path. Then I will come to them from before them and behind them, from their right and their left . . .

(7:16-7)

What Shaytan will say on the Day of Judgement

And Shaytan will say when the matter is decided: surely Allah promised you the promise of truth; and I gave you promises then failed to keep them; I had no authority over you except that I called you and you listened to me, therefore do not blame but blame yourselves...

(14:22)

Seek refuge in Allah from Shaytan

And say: O my Lord! I seek refuge in You from the evil suggestions of the Shaytans.

Such a great enemy needs strong defence doesn't it? How would you defend yourself from the suggestions of Shaytan?

Majeed goes for a picnic

Majeed's _____ was taking their class for a picnic. His mother

packed him some _____, a _____ and a _____.

The day was bright and _____. The students played

_____ and _____. When it was lunchtime the teacher

brought _____ for everybody. Majeed knew he could not eat it, as

the _____ from which it was made was not slaughtered according to

اسلام _____. "But no-one will know" someone whispered in his

_____ "Your _____ is so cold". Majeed looked around. Who

was whispering to him? "Come on, Majeed" the voice said again. "Your mother will

never know." Suddenly Majeed knew who it was. I am going to _____

Shaytan, he told himself. I will not eat najis _____. Even if mum

won't know, Allah will, for Allah knows everything.

The Zabiha (Sacrifice)

All Pilgrims sacrifice an animal on the 10th of Zilhijjah. The sacrifice is done in the memory of Nabi Ibrahim (a). Many Muslims also carry out the sacrifice in their own cities and towns.

Some Questions

?

> **Why do pilgrims have to sacrifice an animal to Allah?**
> **Does Allah need that animal?**

A Allah does not need that animal. But He asks us to scarifice as a sign of piety. The scarifice is an obedience to Allah. Allah says in the Qur'an.

There does not reach Allah their flesh, nor their blood, but to Him reaches the piety from you...

(22:37)

?

> **Is it not a waste to kill so many animals?**

A The meat from the animals is not wasted. Pilgrims are supposed to eat a little from it themselves and give the rest to the poor. Allah says in the Qur'an:

. . . then eat of them [the sacrificed animals] and feed the distressed one, the needy.

(22:28)

Below are pictures of the animals which can be sacrificed on Eid al-Adha.
Write the name of each animal under its picture.

_____   _____   _____   _____

Think and Write

_____

_____

_____

_____

_____

_____

Prophet Ibrahim was ready to sacrifice his beloved son Isma`il for the sake of Allah. Isma`il was his only son, born after very many years of having no children, and Nabi Ibrahim loved him dearly. What do we learn from this great act of the "Friend of Allah"?

A Sacrifice of Sleep

Ammar wished his _____ would stop that awful noise. It was only

_____ and he could hardly open his _____. He dug deeper into his

_____. His mother came to wake him up. "wake up, Ammar" she said.

"It's time for you to _____. "Why do I have to wake up so early?" groaned

Ammar. "Even the _____ isn't out yet." Ammar had been

_____ till late at night. Now he just wanted to sleep in his cozy _____.

"Ammar" said his mum. "You can go to sleep after your _____. Is it too much

to ask that you give up your sleep for _____? Do you know how much Muslims

around the _____ are sacrificing for Islam? They give up their _____

and their _____, their _____, and sometimes even their lives

Do you think it is too much to sacrifice your _____ to pray to Allah?"

A Map of the places of Hajj

The map below shows the places a Haji will visit. Look carefully at each place. Then fill in the sentences below.

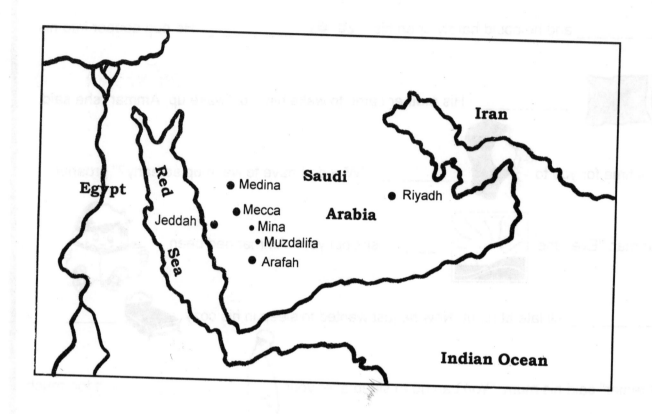

1. Most Hajis land in _____ first, and then go to other places.

2. The first place they visit after that is _____ to perform the Tawaf.

3. On the 9th of Zilhijjah the Hajis go to _____ where they will stay till Maghrib.

4. After Maghrib on the 9th of Zijhijjah, the pilgrims move on to _____ .

5. Early in the morning on the 10th of Zilhajj the pilgrims go to _____

PUZZLE

Yususf is packing to go for hajj. Which items do you think he should not take with him?

Did you Know . .

The Hajj is the largest yearly gathering of people on the earth!!!

Find the route to the Ka'bah

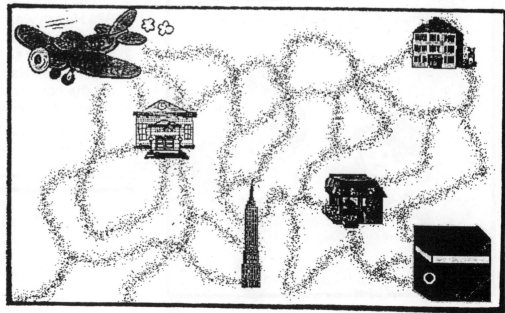

29

All these boys in Ihram look the same. Only two are really exactly the same. Can you find them?

Karim wants to pop some of the balloons. The remaining balloons will join to form the name of the place where Shaytan came to Nabi Ibrahim three times. Which balloons will he pop?

P
M
N
A
S
I

...a d

Use a word ending with **ad** to complete these sentences.

1. Bibi Hajrah was so _____ when she found water for her son.
2. Shaytan was so _____ when he tried to stop Nabi Ibrahim from carrying out the command of Allah.
3. When a Muslim visits the ka'bah, he is so _____ when he has to return home.

Khaleel gets a letter

Khaleel is so excited! His father has gone for Hajj and
Khaleel has just received a letter from him.
He can't wait to read it.
Would you like to read the letter from Mecca with him?

Dear Khaleel,

Salamun Alaykum
I hope you are well, by the Grace of the Almighty. I also
hope that you are doing well in school.

I have a lot to tell you when I get back from Hajj. It has
been a wonderful experience. We returned from Mina
yesterday, after fighting the Shaytan. I hit him as hard as I
could. I shall perform the Tawaf al-Widah tomorrow and
leave for Jeddah, from where I shall Inshallah fly home.

We have been living a very different life for the past few
days. It felt good to see how so many thousands of Muslims
could look all the same. We have been living in tents, and
sleeping on mattresses or sleeping bags. I have not worn
shoes or used perfume for some days now.

I am looking forward to see you Inshallah when you come to
the airport. Don't be surprised to see a different me. I am
now completely bald! At least I won't have to worry about
combing my hair for some time now.

With Salaams,
Your loving father Ammar.

Confused  Khaleel!

Khaleel is so confused. He can't understand some things in his father's letter.
Can you answer some of the questions he has? Otherwise he will have to wait
until his father returns and explains things to him.

1. Who has his father been fighting with in Mina? Khaleel knows that his father
always tells him not to fight with others. Why was he himself fighting and hitting
others?

_____

_____

2. What is Tawaf al-Widah?

_____

3. Why has his father been living in tents? Khaleel thought he had booked a hotel in
Mecca. Was his father camping there?

_____

_____   _____

4. What was his father wearing on his feet, if not his shoes? Why didn't he wear the
shoes he took with him when he left for Mecca?

_____

_____

5. Khaleel couldn't believe that his father was now bald. Why did he do that? Was
that a necessary part of Hajj?

_____

Would you like to receive a letter from Mecca?
Tell some-one going for Hajj to write to you.
Sure would be exciting to get a letter from a Hajj!

Fly a Kite!

Draw a string from each kite to its correct question

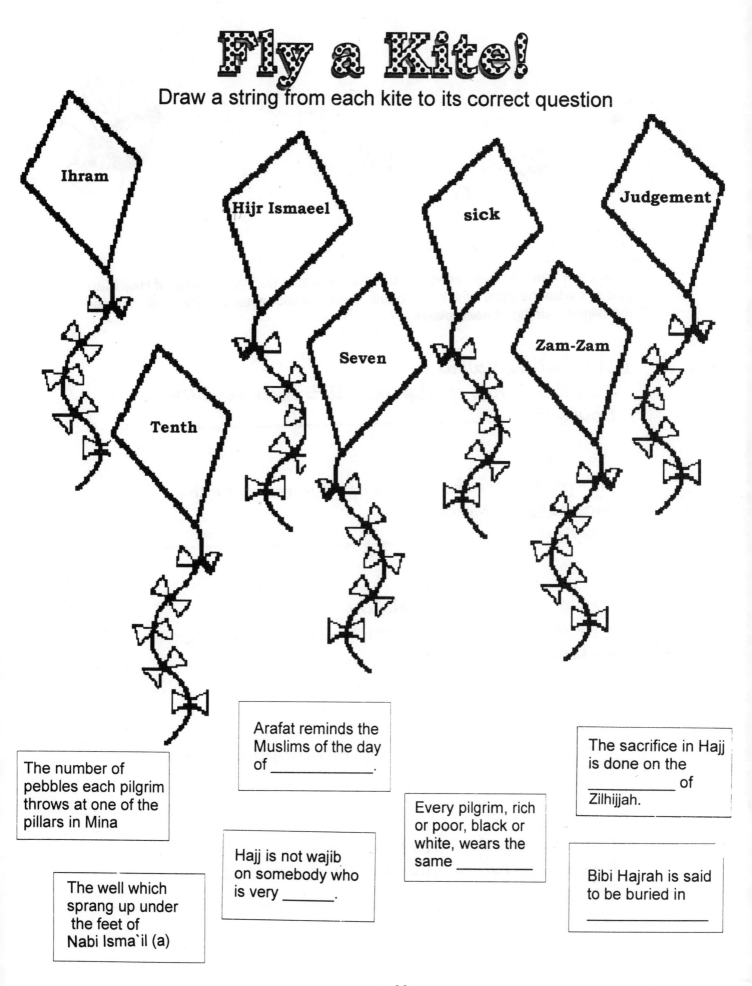

Ihram

Hijr Ismaeel

sick

Judgement

Seven

Zam-Zam

Tenth

Arafat reminds the Muslims of the day of _____ .

The sacrifice in Hajj is done on the _____ of Zilhijjah.

The number of pebbles each pilgrim throws at one of the pillars in Mina

Every pilgrim, rich or poor, black or white, wears the same _____

Hajj is not wajib on somebody who is very _____ .

Bibi Hajrah is said to be buried in _____

The well which sprang up under the feet of Nabi Isma`il (a)

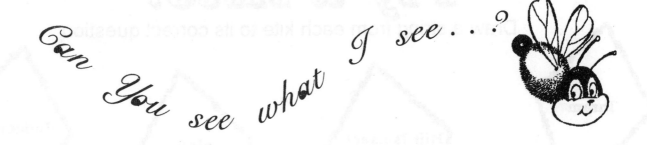

Can You see what I see...?

Adam is a bee who happened to be in Saudi Arabia during the days of Hajj. Can you see what he sees? Fill in the blank sentence with what you think he may see the pilgrims doing at each place.

1. Around the Ka'bah
   I see thousands of pilgrims, all dressed in white
   Doing the _____

2. At Arafah I see thousands of pilgrims, near the
   mountain of Mercy
   Praying for _____

3. I follow them to Muzdalifah
   I see thousands of pilgrims, united and strong
   Picking _____

4. From there I go to Mina
   I see thousands of pilgrims, chanting the Takbir
   Throwing _____

5. I return with the Hajis to Mecca
   I see thousands of pilgrims, devoted to God
   Doing _____

Separate the Apples

Some of the apples below are rotten. They have a False sentence written on them. The good, juicy apples have a True sentence written on them. Circle the good apples and put a cross on the rotten ones.

Hajj is wajib on a Muslim every year if he can afford it

Ihram must be worn at Mecca

The staying in Arafat is known as Wuqoof

Sura al-Feel talks about the elephants of Abraha

A Muslim can only be better than another Muslim if he is more pious (God-fearing)

The Prophet went for his last Hajj in 10 A.H.

Masjid an-Nabi is the Mosque of the Holy Prophet (s)

Pilgrims throw pebbles at the two pillars in Muzdalifa

Taqseer means to sacrifice an animal on the 10th of Zilhajj

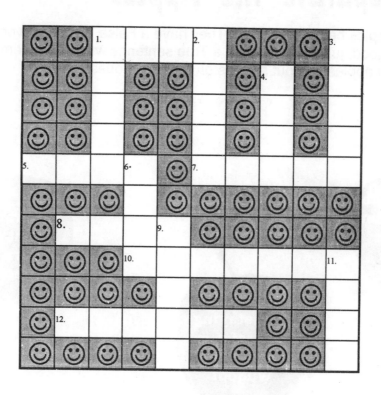

ACROSS

1. Hajrah ran from _____ to Marwa in search of water.
5. Isma`il and Ishaq are the _____ of Nabi Ibrahim (a)
7. Nabi Ibrahim saw a _____ in which Allah told him to sacrifice his son.
8. A Haji walks and sometimes _____ between Safa and Marwa

10. _____ came three times to stop Nabi Ibrahim from sacrificing his son.
12. While in Ihram a Haji cannot kill any animal, not even an _____

DOWN

1. The Tawaf of the Ka'ba means going around it _____ times.
2. Hajar al- _____ is the black stone sent from Heaven for the Ka'ba.
3. _____ Ibrahim, near the Ka'ba has the footsteps of Nabi Ibrahim.

4. Hajj is wajib only _____ in a lifetime.

6. According to the Prophet (s) one who performs Hajj becomes free of _____.

9. One of the animals which can be sacrificed at Hajj.
11. A part of this can be cut at Taqseer.

Wacky Riddles!!

Help Jameel solve these riddles.

1. I am white in color.
   All pilgrims, black or white, rich or poor, need me.
   I remind pilgrims of equality and unity.
   What am I? _____

2. I am wide and long.
   Pilgrims come to me for half a day.
   I remind pilgrims of the Day of Judgement when they will stand
   before their Lord.
   Where am I? _____

3. I was an obedient servant of Allah, willing to be left alone in a
   strange place.
   I am buried near the house of Allah.
   I remind pilgrims of trust and faith in Allah.
   Who am I? _____

4. I am part of the Ka'bah.
   Pilgrims start and end their tawaf at my location.
   I remind pilgrims of heaven.
   What am I? _____

5. I am near Mecca
   Pilgrims come to me on the 10th of Zilhijjah
   I remind pilgrims of their continuous fight against the Shaytan.
   Where am I? _____

6. I am the Friend of Allah.
   I was tested with a most difficult test.
   I remind pilgrims of sacrifice and devotion to the cause of Allah.
   Who am I? _____

Hungry Bunnies

Help these hungry bunnies find some food to eat. Find the vegetables which have the right letters to form the answer for each bunny. Unscramble the letters to form the right answer.

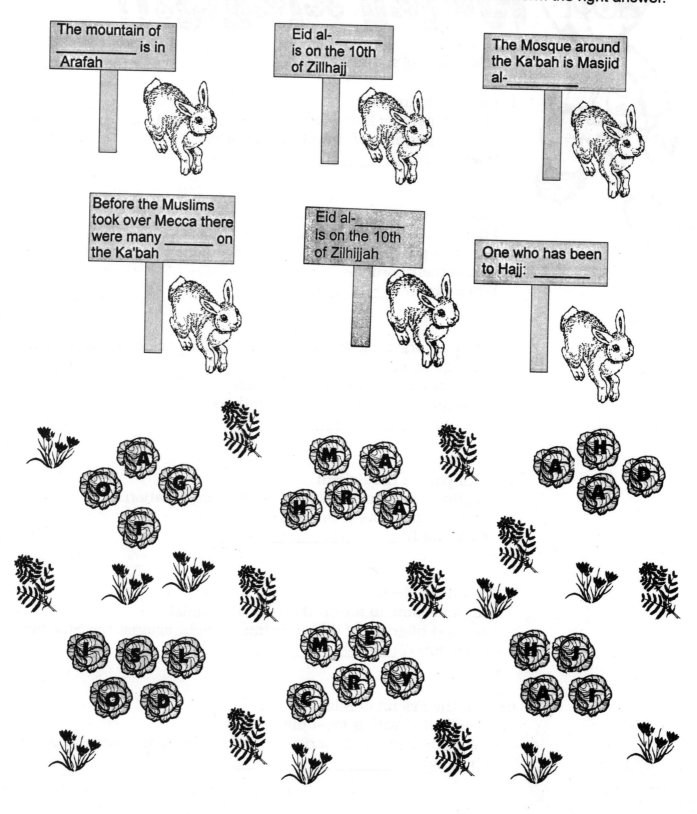

The mountain of
_____ is in
Arafah

Eid al-_____
is on the 10th
of Zillhajj

The Mosque around
the Ka'bah is Masjid
al-_____

Before the Muslims
took over Mecca there
were many _____ on
the Ka'bah

Eid al-_____
is on the 10th
of Zilhijjah

One who has been
to Hajj: _____

Once upon a time there was a King named Abraha. He was the king of Yemen. Abraha wanted that he should be famous and respected. He hated the Ka'bah and did not want people to visit it. He decided to build a huge and beautiful temple in Yemen so people would come to it instead of the Ka'bah. Many people worked very hard to build his temple.

When the temple was finished, Abraha was very proud of it. He spent a lot of money decorating it with gold and precious stones. "Now this house of worship is much better than the simple Ka'bah" he said to himself. "Everyone will now come to worship at my temple." Abrahah ordered that people should come and pray at his temple. Some people, however, thought the Ka'bah, built by Nabi Ibraheem, was holier. They continued going to the Ka'bah. Abraha was angry at that and told his soldiers to stop people from going to Mecca. But people would not listen to them. The Ka'bah was still always surrounded by people, while Abraha's temple was only visited by a few.

Abraha got angrier and angrier. His temple was not getting famous. People did not respect his orders. One day, some people set fire to Abraha's temple. These people were very annoyed with Abraha. How dare he stop them from visiting the house of Allah! Now Abraha was furious. He would have to do something quickly to stop people from visiting the Ka'bah.

Abraha decided that he would destroy the Ka'bah completely. Then no-one wold be able to worship there. He prepared a huge army of elephants, horses and camels and set off for Mecca. The soldiers of Abraha were very sure that nothing could stop them. They had a huge army. They had elephants in the army! Who would be able to fight against them?

The news that Abraha was coming with a huge army spread throughout Mecca. The Meccans were so afraid! Many of them had never seen elephants before. What could they do? Abdul Muttalib, the grandfather of the Holy Prophet (s) was the chief of Mecca at that time. He was not worried. "The Ka'bah has an owner" he said. "The owner Himself will protect it". The Meccans left the city and took shelter in the mountains. They waited to see what would happen.

Abraha's huge army started marching towards the Ka'bah. The huge elephants, with soldiers sitting upon them, were ready to attack the Ka'bah. Suddenly a dark cloud was seen in the sky. The cloud came nearer! It was a huge flock of tiny birds. Each bird had small stones in its beak and feet. When the birds were directly above Abraha's army, they began to shower them with the stones. The stones hit so hard that people fell off from the animals they were sitting on. The elephants panicked and started running. Many animals and soldiers died in the panic. Others fled as they tried to escape the falling stones.

The Meccans watched in joy as the army of Abraha ran away from the Ka'bah. They had failed in their effort to destroy the Ka'bah. Allah had protected His house from the enemies.

All of Arabia came to know about Abraha's attack and defeat. His huge army of elephants had been destroyed by small birds. No-one has more power than Allah, and those who are His enemies will always be defeated.

The year in which this event took place was then recorded as "Aamul Feel" or the "Year of the Elephant." This was the year 570 A.D. It was in the same year that the grandson of Abdul Muttalib was born. His name was Muhammad, and he would grow up to be the great Prophet of Islam.

Sura al-Feel (Sura No: 105)

Allah talks about the event of the elephants in Sura al-Feel. He says:

In the name of Allah, the Beneficent, the Merciful.
1. Have you not seen how your Lord dealt with the people of the elephants?
2. Did he not cause their plot to go astray?
3. And He sent down upon them birds in flocks.
4. Striking them with stones of baked clay.
5. So he made them like straw eaten up.

(105:1-5)

Now answer the following questions

See how much you remember!

1. Why did Abraha hate the Ka'bah?

_____

_____

2. What made people know that the Ka'bah was holier than the temple of Abraha?

_____

_____

3. Why were the Meccans so afraid of the elephants, and how did Abdul Muttalib calm them?

_____

_____

_____

4. Look up Sura al-Feel in the Qur'an. What is the Arabic word for the birds which destroyed the elephants of Abraha?

_____

5. Describe in one sentence what you learn from this story.

_____

Join the Hands

Join each part of section A to a part in Section B to form a complete sentence

Going for Hajj   is the black stone in the Ka'bah.

The Ka'bah   between 8th and 13th of Zilhijjah.

Hajrah was the wife of the Nabi Ibraheem   perform the Hajj every year.

Every year Hajj takes place   is the dream of every Muslim.

Hajar al-Aswad   was built by Nabi Ibrahim and Nabi Isma`il

The well which sprang up under the baby feet of Nabi Isma`il   who ran 7 times between Safa and Marwa in search of water.

More than two million Muslims   visit Medina.

After Hajj many pilgrims   increases unity and brotherhood among Muslims.

Performing the Hajj with so many other Muslims   is known as Zamzam.

The Believers are but brethren (brothers and sisters) so make peace between your brethren
Holy Qur'an 49:10

Stories of Nabi Ibrahim (a)

In the Holy Quran Allah talks about Nabi Ibrahim in many places. You have probably heard some of his stories. Look at the pictures below. Read the verse of the Quran written beside it. Then write that story of Nabi Ibrahim in your own words.

21: 57-63

21: 68-70

Some Du'as of Nabi Ibrahim (a)

Nabi Ibrahim was a very devoted servant of Allah. He often prayed to Allah and his prayers have been mentioned in the Holy Qur'an. Many of his prayers can be found in Sura Ibrahim, sura no:14.

Read the following Du'as. Try to memorize these du'as and recite them often.

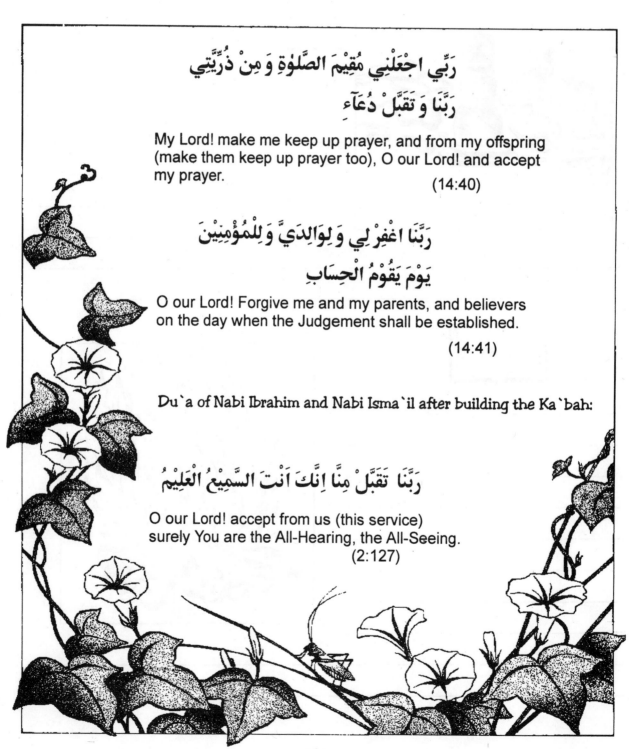

رَبِّ اجْعَلْنِي مُقِيمَ الصَّلوٰةِ وَ مِنْ ذُرِّيَّتِي

رَبَّنَا وَ تَقَبَّلْ دُعَاءِ

My Lord! make me keep up prayer, and from my offspring (make them keep up prayer too), O our Lord! and accept my prayer.

(14:40)

رَبَّنَا اغْفِرْ لِي وَ لِوَالِدَيَّ وَ لِلْمُؤْمِنِيْنَ

يَوْمَ يَقُوْمُ الْحِسَابِ

O our Lord! Forgive me and my parents, and believers on the day when the Judgement shall be established.

(14:41)

Du'a of Nabi Ibrahim and Nabi Isma'il after building the Ka'bah:

رَبَّنَا تَقَبَّلْ مِنَّا إِنَّكَ اَنْتَ السَّمِيْعُ الْعَلِيْمُ

O our Lord! accept from us (this service) surely You are the All-Hearing, the All-Seeing.
(2:127)

A shorter word

The words underlined can be replaced with one of the words from the box. Find the
correct word and write it at the end of each sentence. You can also add words such as *do,
the* etc. to make a proper sentence.

Talbiyah
Tawaf
Sa'ee

Kiswah
Umrah
Ihram

1. Every Haji puts on <u>white cloth, unsewn pieces for men, and simple clothes for
women which cover them fully.</u> _____

2. When the Hajis reach the Ka'bah, they <u>go around it seven times.</u> _____

3. The Ka'bah is covered with <u>a thick black cloth embroidered with verses from
the Holy Qur'an.</u> _____

4. In memory of Bibi Hajrah, the Hajis <u>run seven times between safa and
Marwah.</u> _____

5. When they near the Ka'bah, the pilgrims recite: *Labbaik Allahumma Labbaik,
Labbaik La Shareeka laka Labbaik, Innal hamda wan ne'mata laka wal mulk, la
shareeka laka.* _____

6. When it is not time for Hajj, Muslims can still go to Mecca to <u>wear the Ihram,
perform the Tawaf and Sae'e, and do the Taqseer.</u> _____

An Ayat on Equality

All Muslims are equal in the eyes of Allah. Allah only loves the one who is most pious, and obedient to Him. The Holy Prophet (s) often told the Muslims that there was no difference between Muslims of different races. Allah does not look at the color or the appearance of people. He created them all and loves them all. He looks at the hearts and deeds of people, and loves most the one who is careful of his duty to Allah.

Color the verse below. The verse is found in Sura al-Hujurat of the Holy Qur'an. The verse number is 49:13. Look it up in your Qur'an.

O Mankind we have created

you from a male and a female

and made you into

tribes and nations

that you may know each other,

Surely the most honorable of

you with Allah is the most pious.

Pilgrims from around the world

Pilgrims from all over the world gather in Mecca for Hajj. Let us interview three different pilgrims about their country. Fill in the blanks in the conversations by looking at the boxes on the next page.

1. Brother Akram comes from Egypt

Q Assalamu alaykum Br. Akram. You come from Egypt. How many Muslims are there in Egypt?

A Alaikumus Salaam. The population of Egypt is more than _____ and _____ % of the people of Egypt are Muslims.

Q What is the official language of Egypt?

A The official language is _____

Q What is the currency of Egypt?

A The currency of Egypt is the _____.

2. Sister Shahidah comes from Malaysia.

Q. Assalamu Alaykum Sr. Shahidah. You come from Malaysia. In which continent is Malaysia?

A. Alaikumus salaam. Malaysia is in _____

Q. How many Muslims are there in Malaysia?

A. There are more than _____ Muslims living in Malaysia.

Q. What is the capital of Malaysia?

A. The capital of Malaysia is _____.

3. Br. Abdul comes from Jordan.

Q. Assalamu Alaykum Br. Abdul. You come from Jordan. Have you come a long way?

A. _____

Q. What percentage of Jordanians are Muslims?

A. Almost _____ of Jordanians are Muslims.

Q. What is the capital of Jordan?

A. _____ is the capital of Jordan.

Islamic  Countries

EGYPT

Continent: Africa
Neighbours: Libya, Sudan, Palestine
Population: Over 47 million
Muslim percentage of population: 94
Capital: Cairo
Official language: Arabic
Currency: Egyptian Pound
Climate: Mostly hot.

MALAYSIA

Continent: Asia
Neighbours: Brunei, Indonesia, Thailand.
Population: Over 15.5 million
Muslim percentage of population: 41%
Capital: Kuala Lampur
Official language: Malay
Currency: Malaysian dollar
Climate: Warm and humid

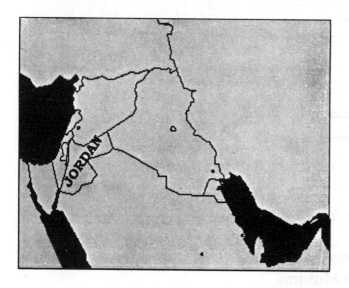

JORDAN

Continent: Asia
Neighbours: Syria, Iraq, Saudi Arabia
Population: Almost 4 million
Muslim percentage of population: 91%
Capital: Amman
Official language: Arabic
Currency: Jordanian Dinar
Climate: Mainly hot

Can you look for some other Islamic countries in the maps above?
Check your atlases and look for:
Sudan, Morocco, Indonesia, Iraq, Syria, Iran and Saudi Arabia.

Scrambled names

The following names of great people in Islamic history are scrambled.
Read the sentence below each name and then unscramble the letters.
Write the correct name in the blank.

1. HCIAAS _____
The son of Nabi Ibrahim from his wife Sarah.

2. LLIAB _____
When the Muslims took over Mecca he climbed the Ka'bah to give adhan.

3. MAILASI _____
The son of Nabi Ibrahim from whom the holy Prophet (s) is descended.

4. RAAJHH _____
The mother of Nabi Isma`il

5. RHMAIIB _____
Allah says in the Qur'an (3:67) that he was neither a Jew nor a Christian, but
he was a true believer, a Muslim

6. DUAMHMAM _____
The Prophet who ordered that all the idols on the Ka'bah should be destroyed.

7. RBAAAH _____
The man who came with an army of elephants to destroy the Ka'bah in the year
the Prophet was born.

8. HNU _____
During this Prophet's time there was a great flood, and the Ka'bah had to be
rebuilt after that.

49

Answers

Page 3

Question One: 1. b)Mecca 2. c)Maqam Ibrahim
3. a)Tawaf 4. b) Baitullah.

Question Two: 1. Good health, money, someone to look after his/her children, home etc.
2. 8th to 13th Zilhajj
3. The distressed and the needy.

Question Three: 1. False 2.False 3.True

Page 4

1. Cube 2.Nabi Ibrahim and Nabi Isma`il 3.Kiswah
4.Hajr al-Aswad 5. Heaven 6. Masjidul Haram

Page 5

Baitul Muqaddas, A compass, When a Muslim is dying and when slaughtering an animal, The prayer is broken.

Page 7

Black stone, Jibrael, Tawaf, Kiss, Touch.

Page 8

MAQAM IBRAHIM 1.Nabi Ibrahim. 2.Building the Ka'bah
3.Pray after Tawaf.

Page 11

1. 30 years old. 2. Repairing the Ka'bah. 3. Al-Amin
4. He asked all the leaders of the tribes to raise a piece of cloth on which he put the Hajar al-Aswad. Then he himself put it in place.

Page 13

1. You have no partner. 2. Labbaik.

Page 15

Question One: 1. Hajj, Umra. 2. Niyyah. 3. Two. 4. Bodies and hair
5.Perfume and shoes.

Question Two: 1.Wrong 2. Wrong 3. Correct 4. Wrong 5. Wrong

Page16

1. Mustahab. 2. Widah 3. Qur'an, Dhikr 4. 14
5. 2 Raka'at parayer 6.Good of this world and the Hereafter

Page 20

1. 80 2. 150 3. 49 4. 147 5. 15 6. 12 7. 3

Page 25

1. Jeddah   2. Mecca   3. Arafah   4. Muzdalifa   5. Mina

Page 29

1. His father fought with Shaytan, as he is an enemy of man. It is done in the memory of Nabi Ibrahim's fight against Shaytan.

2. The last Tawaf a pilgrim does before leaving for home.

3. Pilgrims live in tents in Arafah, Mina and Muzdalifa.

4. He was wearing sandals as shoes are not allowed in Ihram.

5. Shaving off part or all of the hair is part of Taqseer.

Page 31

1. Tawaf   2. Mercy and Forgiveness.   3. Pebbles

4. Pebbles at the pillars.   5. The Tawaf.

Page 33

Across: 1.Safa 5.Sons 7.Dream 8. Runs 10.Shaytan 12.Insect

Down:1.Seven 2.Aswad 3.Maqam 4.Once 6.Sins 9.Sheep 11.Nail

Page 34

1.Ihram 2.Arafah 3.Hajrah 4.Hajar al-Aswad 5.Mina 6. Ibrahim

Page 38

1. He wanted to be famous and respected himself.

2. It was built by Nabi Ibrahim.

3. They had never seen elephants before. Abdul Muttalib told them the owner of the Ka'bah would protect it.

4. Ababil.   5. The Power of Allah is Great.

Page 42

1.Ihram 2. Tawaf 3.Kiswah 4. Sa'ee 5.Talbiyyah 6. Umra

Page 44

1.47 million, 94, Arabic, Egyptian Pound.

2. Asia, 6 million, Kuala Lampur

3. No, I live close by, 91, Amman.

Page 46

1. ISHAAQ 2.BILAL 3.ISMAIL 4.HAJRAH 5.IBRAHIM
6.MUHAMMAD 7.ABRAHA 8.NUH

Goodword**kidz**

Helping you build a family of faith

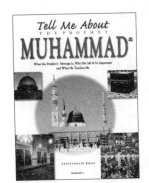

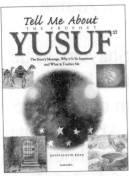

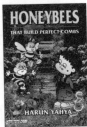

Goodword Books Pvt. Ltd.

1, Nizamuddin West Market, New Delhi 110 013

Tel. (9111) 2435 6666, 2435 5454 Fax (9111) 2435 7333, 2435 7980 E-mail: info@goodwordbooks.com

www.goodwordbooks.com

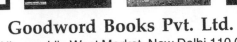